OVER THE LINE

AN INTRODUCTION
TO **POETRY COMICS**

EDITED BY

Chrissy Williams & Tom Humberstone

sidekickBOOKS

www.sidekickbooks.com

This is a first edition published in 2015 by
SIDEKICK BOOKS
www.sidekickbooks.com

Printed on UPM offset FSC certified paper
with biodegradable inks by Calverts.coop

The print process is powered by a 100%
renewable energy tariff from Ecotricity.

Typeset in Quicksand.
The Sidekick Books logo uses Roman Antique.

Cover art by Ioan Morris
Art direction by Tom Humberstone

ISBN 978-1-909650-02-4

Supported using public funding by
ARTS COUNCIL
ENGLAND
LOTTERY FUNDED

contents

i. some introductions

preface

"Poetry Comics" is a term that came into use following the New York School experiments of the 1960s, but in particular after a book called *Poetry Comics* was published by American writer, artist and educator Dave Morice in 1980. Notably, he took classic poems and broke them into sequences of panels to create poem comics.

In his introduction to *Poetry Comics*, Morice talks about the explosive growth of the comic strip in the early part of the 20th Century, noting the simultaneous growth of the little magazine while giving specific mention to poetry journals (e.g. *Poetry*, *Blast*). If visual art up to this point had been largely confined to perspectives from a single fixed standpoint, Cubism showed that this no longer had to be the case. The effects of splintering and fragmentation that grew out of Cubism and Modernism had profound effects on what we now understand to be modern art and literature, modern comics and modern poetry. Poetry got the perceived highbrow end of the stick, and comics the low. The idea of bringing the two mediums together therefore serves as a metaphor for the increasing democratisation of artforms that we see occuring around us. Cross-artform collaborations are more and more common. The similarities and differences between mediums are ripe for exploration. For the curious, everything has the potential for artistic value.

Despite it being over twenty years since Art Spiegelman's *Maus* won the Pulitzer Prize, comics still have something of an image problem. Even more recent awards such as Mary Talbot's Costa Prize win or Alison Bechdel's MacArthur Foundation Grant Award don't seem to prevent the mainstream media from continuing to align comics with child audiences and the superhero genre. It remains all too easy for an unassuming public to go on mistaking bold lines and garish colours for crudeness of content.

In fact what appears often to be 'simplistic' in the cartooning style is evoking the universal resonance of the icon, just as many corporations and organisations employ recognisable logos which go beyond representation. It could be said that the more cartoony the illustration, the broader its signifying capabilities. Comics creator and theorist Scott McCloud says: "The cartoon is a vacuum into which our identity and awareness are pulled... an empty shell that we inhabit, which enables us to travel in another realm. We don't just observe the cartoon, we become it."[1]

If comics have an image problem, then poetry's problem may be that it has no modern image to speak of, or at least not one that extends far beyond the poetry world. For many it is experienced most frequently at weddings and funerals, and retains something of the weight and solemnity associated with the need to communicate complex emotions. It's not a bad image to have, but it's not a very lively one. Poetry can and does escape this perceived oppressive weight, and we hope this anthology may be a way for those unused to reading poetry (as well as those who are) to experience its capacity for play.

Poet, artist and Poetry Comics creator Bianca Stone says: "The poetry comic form can demand you to stop and inspect the intricacies of the image, while also taking in the meaning of the words. In other words, you're being both propelled forward and stalled simultaneously."[2] We find this to be excellent advice in terms of the way Poetry Comics are best experienced. Both image and text must be read and digested, at your own pace, in your own way.

What follows is a playful introductory exploration of the poetry and comics mediums, as well as some existing practitioners of Poetry Comics, followed by a showcase of new work that we hope will inspire more to follow.

Chrissy Williams
Tom Humberstone

---

1 *Understanding Comics*, Scott McCloud, 1993
2 Bianca Stone, "The Internet Is a Poetry Comic", *The Georgia Review*, 1/7/2015

introduction

Comics don't need the implied gravitas of poetry in order to be taken seriously.

David Troupes, from *Buttercup Festival*

To explain in words precisely what happens between the last two panels above, whether literally, figuratively or emotionally, would take far longer than the few seconds it takes the eye to read the artwork. The earlier text adds to the effects of the art, planting seeds of familiarity, superstition, love, ritual and emotion, but it is the artwork that transports us far across space and time – complexity in a single panel transition.

Poems don't need pictures, or the implied popularity or supposed 'accessibility' of comics in order to communicate.

'Twas brillig, and the slithy toves
    Did gyre and gimble in the wabe:
All mimsy were the borogoves,
    And the mome raths outgrabe.

"Beware the Jabberwock, my son!
    The jaws that bite, the claws that catch!
Beware the Jubjub bird, and shun
    The frumious Bandersnatch!"

Lewis Carroll, from *Jabberwocky*

What does it mean? What is a Jabberwock? Does it matter that we don't know what colour it is, or what shape? No. The delight is in the words, the rhymes, the playful strangeness and yet simultaneous plausibility of the words. (Did you put extra emphasis on "frumious" without knowing why?) There is music here, which goes beyond meaning. If you read a comic aloud, you kill it. If you read a poem aloud, you bring it to life.

Comics communicate through sequential art. Let's compare their visual language to the language of poetry, with the help of Scott McCloud's excellent introduction, *Understanding Comics*. These examples are not intended to be a like-for-like comparison, but rather to provoke thought on how poems might work.

Moment-to-Moment

In McCloud's example, the woman's eyes are open in panel one, and closed in panel two. We fill in the blank between the panels and deduce she has closed her eyes. Can we think of linebreaks as doing similar things to panelbreaks, in terms of the leap between images? Here, the line divides two parts of the same image:

'Twas brillig, and the slithy toves
Did gyre and gimble in the wabe...

The first line shows the toves. The second shows us what they're doing. What if it were all on one line? How does the linebreak change what we read?

Action-to-Action

This is slightly more complex. The line divides the action into two parts, though they form the same image.

One, two! One, two! And through and through
The vorpal blade went snicker-snack!

The first line gives us the action without verbs – it could be happening in the present tense. The second could stand alone, but builds on this, giving us the sound, and "went", (i.e. the past tense) giving the action a sense of closure.

Do the linebreaks help to guide the reader, to build images incrementally, to show us where to focus?

Comics are often compared to film storyboards, which sells their power short. Comics and poetry can take place in the spaces between lines and words. The reading process isn't always linear. You choose your own pace, where to look, to go back, to linger, and to stop.

Subject-to-Subject

This requires more involvement on the part of the reader:

He left it dead, and with its head
*   He went galumphing back.*

"And, has thou slain the Jabberwock?
*   Come to my arms, my beamish boy!*

Here, one stanza ends with the son's departure after the killing of the Jabberwock. The next begins with direct speech, which we deduce must be his father, despite not being told so explicitly.

How are linebreaks different from stanza breaks (i.e. the breaks between verses)?

Scene-to-Scene

This is quite similar to the "Subject-to-Subject" transition, but with a more significant journey across time and space:

O frabjous day! Callooh! Callay!"
*   He chortled in his joy.*

'Twas brillig, and the slithy toves
*   Did gyre and gimble in the wabe*

The joyous stanza cuts off, and the new stanza transports us back to the original setting, even using the exact same words as the first verse. And yet the scene has been transformed by what we've been through in the poem – a journey across time and space by way of repetition.

McCloud defines two more types of panel transition. There are other poem elements we might consider as well as linebreaks and stanza breaks though. We could look at imagery in general, as well as the transitions and relationships between individual words, and groups of words. What other comparisons might we draw?

Aspect-to-Aspect

This transition involves scene and mood changes – strong images built on specific detail. Look at the following examples of imagistic scene setting, building mood with words even when we're not given their meanings:

'Twas brillig,

↓

and the slithy toves

↓

Did gyre and gimble

↓

in the wabe

Non-Sequiturs

Poetry often does this best when it is creating new images, using unexpected words and juxtapositions. This transition between single words, between music and meaning, is often at the heart of poetry. If you put two words together, your brain will make a connection between them. Let's use these invented adjectives as an example:

wood	→	tulgey wood
foe	→	manxome foe
blade	→	vorpal blade
toves	→	slithy toves

In the same way that it's a mistake to think of comics as 'prose with illustration' rather than being more complex compositions, it's a mistake to think of poems as prose divided into different lines. The way language is used is fundamental to the way poetry communicates.

structure

As we have been seeing – a visual structure of lines and stanzas on the page. This includes spaces between words, and exploring the page in new ways.

syntax

The grammatical order of words on the page – easy or complex? Full sentences or fragments?

register and tone

The types of words and punctuation chosen to create a specific mood. "O frabjous day!" rather than "Oh, not Tuesday…"

rhyme and repetition

Key in the poet's toolkit. E.g. "gyre and gimble" or "toves" and "borogoves". Repetition of words, of letters, of sounds, of structure, of all sorts.

rhythm

Whether regular or irregular, all words carry a music to them. The poet's task is to write it down.

imagery

Similes. Metaphors. Imagery. Are they unusual and "mimsy", or are they predictable and "flat as a pancake", "the last straw", like "flogging a dead horse"?

Let's also think about the way mainstream comics are often made (sometimes by one person, sometimes by a group of people). We can break a comic into different jobs and muse over how those processes might translate into poetry. Of course, not everyone makes comics in this way, just as not everyone makes poems in the same way. What might the other processes be?

script	Can often look like a screenplay, giving descriptions, text and reference.	The idea for the poem, what you imagine the poem to be?
pencil sketches	Artist's first visual rendering of the flow of the page, rough characters, words etc.	Draft lines, wisps of phrasing?
inks	Committing ink to the page. There are no mistakes. Each line is what it is.	Sitting down to assemble the poem into a solid form of some sort?
colour	Adding colour. This is not a small stage. Colour can utterly transform the work.	What do you think it might mean to add colour to a poem?
lettering	Layering the words on top of the artwork. This involves careful attention to space and positioning.	Positioning. This could perhaps be connected to structure on the page, and considering where everything goes?
editing	Choosing which words to lose and what to tweak. Thinking about how all the page elements best interact.	Choosing which words to lose and what to tweak. Thinking about how all the page elements best interact.

Let's consider a few final statements that may be useful in drawing comparisons between the two mediums:

economy of line is paramount

each panel and page must be carefully constructed

consider how much will fit on the page

put everything in its right place

choose whether to prioritise ideas or form

juxtaposition is an important tool

composition is not linear, but a whole
system of architecture

the reading process is one of interpretation
rather than perception

the reader is inextricable from the art

all the right notes, not necessarily in the right order

what happens off the page is as important
as what happens on it

the impossible can be made possible

practitioners

There are many artists already working in this fruitful area, some who are actively calling it Poetry Comics or Comics Poetry, and others who are not. The following section serves as an introduction to their work.

It may be useful at this point to say a few words about what we have not included. We haven't included examples of long poems which have been reimagined as whole comics (such as Martin Rowson's *The Waste Land*, Eric Drucker's *Howl: A Graphic Novel*, Dave Morice's or Julian Peters' work, or the much-lauded anthology of World War I poems reinterpreted into comics: *Above the Dreamless Dead*). Neither have we included examples of purely illustrative poems, where the images serve largely to repeat or reinforce what the text is doing, such as Alice Oswald's *Weeds and Wild Flowers* or Tim Burton's *The Melancholy Death of Oyster Boy*. We haven't included notable comics which show characters or captions in verse, such as Neil Gaiman's *Sandman*, Alan Moore's *Swamp Thing* or Matt Fraction's *ODY-C*. We also haven't included any comics about poetry, such as Harvey Pekar's excellent *The Beats: A Graphic History*. We would however recommend all these works highly.

We also haven't included any of the precursers to contemporary Poetry Comics, for example the New York School's anthology series *C: Comics*, in which poets such as Joe Brainard, John Ashbery and Frank O'Hara collaborated on poetry and comics work, or Joe Brainard's *The Nancy Book*. Kenneth Koch's *The Art of the Possible* is a wonderful introduction to a poet playing with text and panel structure in the absence of artwork. Kenneth Patchen's final works can be likened to those of William Blake's, combining image and poetry in phantasmagoric sequence. Finally, the recent groudbreaking *Antigonick*, a "comic-book presentation of Sophokles' *Antigone*" by poet Anne Carson with art by Bianca Stone, disrupts the reading process with vellum pages which move back and forth across each other and would suffer from representation by a single static image here. Please seek out all these works.

We hope the examples in the subsequent pages will offer a way in to the varying styles, diverse approaches, and breadth of work already being produced.

Ink Brick is a magazine published in New York devoted entirely to Poetry Comics, edited by Alexander Rothman, Paul K. Tunis, Alexey Sokolin, Bianca Stone and Gary Sullivan. (You will find Rothman's work elsewhere in this anthology.) The extract below from Alexey Sokolin's work collages found images with text, using geometrical structure to contrast the emotional tone of the text.

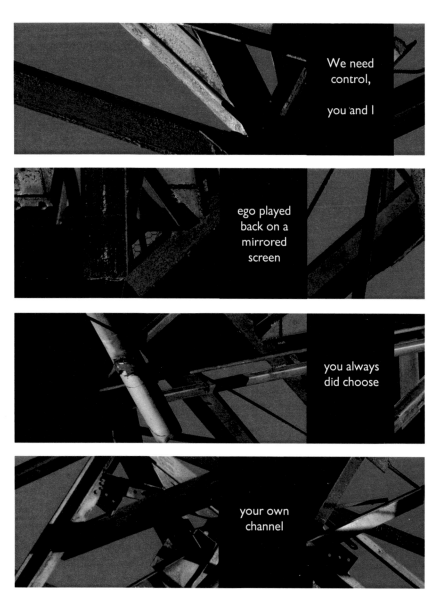

From *Peckish*.

American artist John Hankiewicz also plays with shape and geometry here, but treats the text as an art object, incorporating it more distinctly into the artwork itself. He also uses the lines of the notepaper to enhance the text, for example in the first panel.

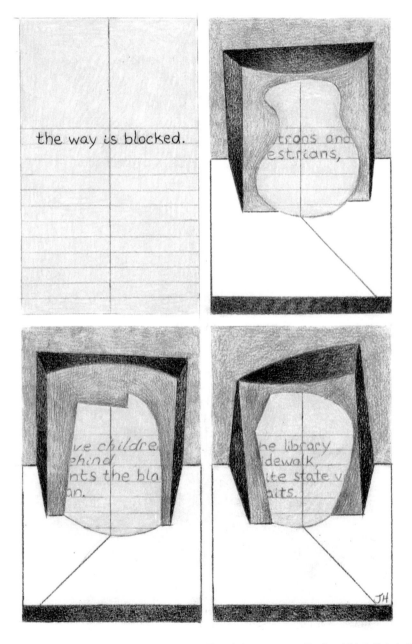

From *The Intermission Festival* (*Ink Brick* #1).

Bianca Stone has published Poetry Comics for a number of years. Notable works include *I Want To Open The Mouth God Gave You*, *Beautiful Mutant* and the aforementioned *Antigonick*. In this example, Stone juxtaposes a single image with text. The text provides the motion down the page we might expect from panel transitions, using linebreaks to guide our eye and modify the image.

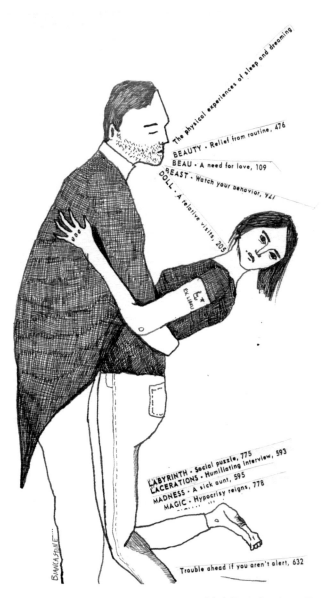

Untitled, Pen/ Ink/ Typewriter.

Paul K. Tunis has a distinctive style, notable for his use of colour, often using coloured blocks to signify panel structure. One of his most notable works is a collaboration with poet Matthea Harvey called *Game for Anything*, which was designed for a scroll-down online reading experience. The sample below is from a piece that was first published in issue 1 of *Ink Brick*.

From *Avenge Me, Eavesdropper* (*Ink Brick* #1).

Derik Badman is among those published in the anthology *Comics as Poetry* (along with Kimball Anderson, William Corbett, Warren Craghead, Julie Delporte, Oliver East, Franklin Einspruch, Jason Overby and Paul K. Tunis). In the example below, he uses a style associated with mid-20th century American romance comics, specifically those of Vince Colletta, and deliberately subverts the reading process. The reader must make active decisions about how to read the work. Although there is a deliberate design, there is no longer a single 'correct' journey through it.

From *Colletta Suite* (*Comics as Poetry*).

Warren Craghead employs a minimalistic style. The text is not demarcated by speech balloons or other means, but is integrated into the artwork, binding the text and art together more strongly. The apparent simplicity of the line draws an iconic but naturalistic force from the work. This sort of approach can also be seen in the work of UK artists such as Simon Moreton and Oliver East.

IF A NOTE NEXT
TO A NOTE

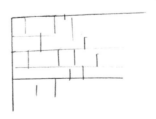

THEN YOU.

From If a Note Next to a Note.

Julie Delporte's work was also featured in the *Comics as Poetry* anthology. The pencil colours and handwritten text in the example below make the piece feel personal and organic, and the text is written in a confessional diary style. The deceptively simple text and images transform each other, while their style and colouring reflect each other.

July 4th
I think about the fox at your parents' in Kamouraska, who I won't be seeing this summer.

it's starting to get hot again.
Time to escape the city.

From *Journal*.

Gary Sullivan is an American artist, also on the editorial board for *Ink Brick.* The example below seems on the surface to be a straightforward cartoony, narrative structure, but its power comes from juxtaposing a casual unassuming tone (in terms of text), with a startling unfolding visual narrative.

From *Black Magic* (*Ink Brick* #1).

UK illustrator and cartoonist Stephen Collins has created works that fall into the category of Poetry Comics. The example below shows his attention to unusual panel structure and transitions.

From *Exit Music* (*Solipsistic Pop* #1).

Dave Troupes's *Buttercup Festival* offsets playful text against a minimalist cartoony art style, and is currently being serialised in UK poetry journal *PN Review*.

From *Buttercup Festival*.

UK artist Louise Crosby has been working with Bloodaxe poet Clare Shaw to create new works. The establishing shot in the first panel here seems straightforward, then the intense zoom in the second and third panels refocuses our attention, drawing out detail.

Louise Crosby and Clare Shaw, from *Poem for a Bus Shelter*.

This example from American poet and artist Sommer Browning demonstrates a play with panel structure in the absence of images in a manner that is reminiscent of Kenneth Koch's work. It asks questions about how panels work, how much you can fit into any one panel, how panel structure is constructed, and how it builds.

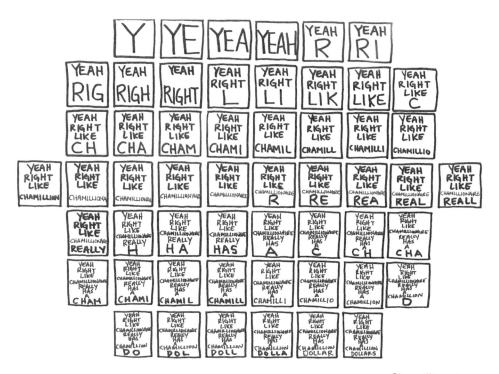

Chamillionaire.

This piece by poet John Canfield, attendee of a regular informal Poetry Comics gathering in London for several years, plays with the notion of panel design, and what a panel might be.

Untitled by John Canfield (*Poetry and Comics*, Issuu.com).

This piece, also created as part of the London group, shows delight in the chaos of placement. It renders the text in layers, one on top of the other, as if the panels might run from front to back rather than from side to side. The additional pencil marks denoting the speech marks are made in colour, as if part of the artwork rather than text, blurring the lines between the two.

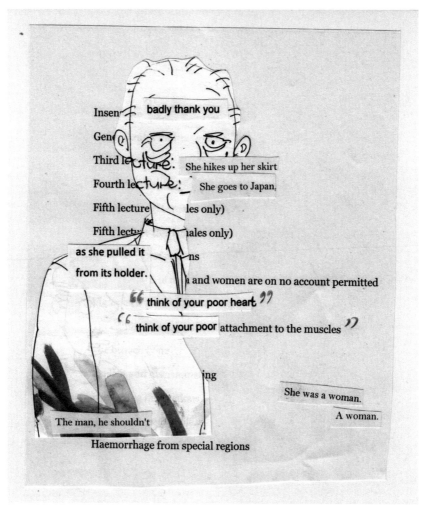

Untitled by Sean Azzopardi and Kirsten Irving
(*Poetry and Comics*, Issuu.com).

This piece juxtaposes poetic text with a more traditional comics form and works by providing a strong visual backdrop the words can resonate with and draw additional power from.

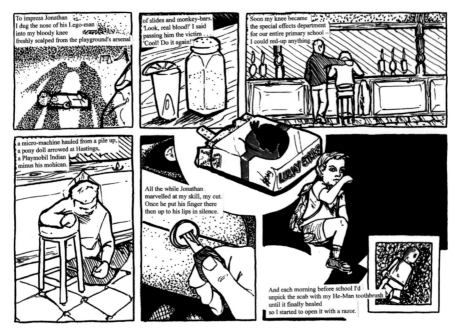

Lego Man by Rob VonRamm and Richard Scott (*Poetry and Comics*, Issuu.com).

This piece breaks a single image across three panels. The image is complete when the piece is looked at as a whole, and yet each part is different when looked at individually: a useful metaphor for the reading process of any comic.

Untitled by Lorraine Mariner (*Poetry and Comics*, Issuu.com).

further reading

Poetry Comics Anthologies
Poetry as Comics, *Ink Brick* magazine, *Solipsistic Pop*,
Poetry & Comics (on issuu.com)

Practitioners
All creators and works mentioned in this introduction,
and in the book at large.

Selected Publishers
Breakdown Press, Factory Hollow Press, Ink Brick, Koyama Press,
New Modern Press, Sidekick Books

Articles
"How to Read Nancy" by Mark Newgarden and Paul Karasik
(1988, http://www.laffpix.com/howtoreadnancy.pdf)

"Poetry, Design and Comics: an interview with SETH"
(*Carousel19*, 2006: Spring/Summer, http://www.
carouselmagazine.ca/assets/C19-seth-excerpt.pdf)

"Comics Poetry, Poetry Comics, Graphic Poems" by Derik Badman
(*The Hooded Utilitarian*, www.hoodedutilitarian.com, August 2012)

"The New York Comics and Picture-Story Symposium: Lior
Zaltzman & Alexander Rothman" by Sophia Wiedeman
(*The Rumpus*, http://therumpus.net, July 2014)

"Poetry Comics, Profluent Lingering, and Two Works by Bianca
Stone" by Robert Loss
(*The Comics Journal*, http://www.tcj.com, March 2015)

"Comics Poetry Toolbox" by Alexander Rothman
(*YouTube*, March 2015)

"What is Comics Poetry?" by Alexander Rothman
(*Indiana Review*, http://indianareview.org Summer 2015)

"The Internet Is a Poetry Comic", interview with Bianca Stone
(*The Georgia Review*, Summer 2015)

ii. new work

PROTOLITHS

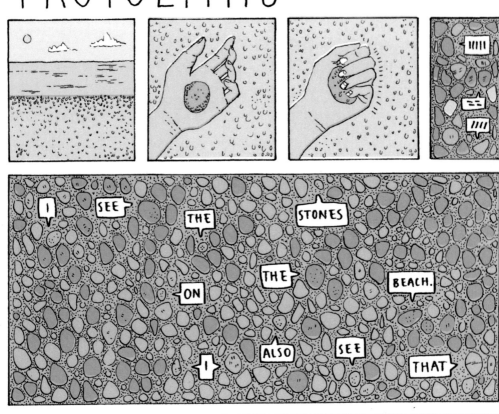

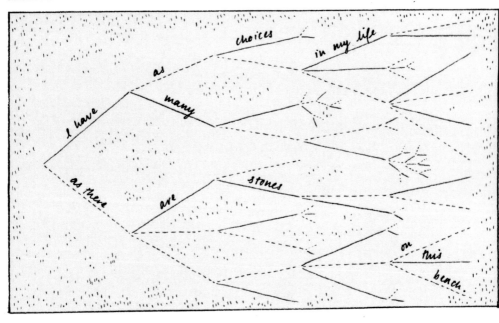

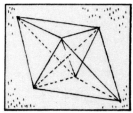
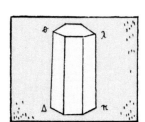
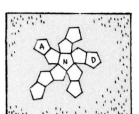

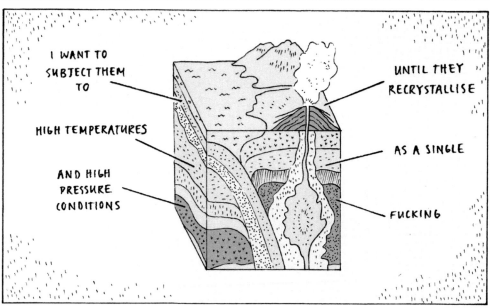

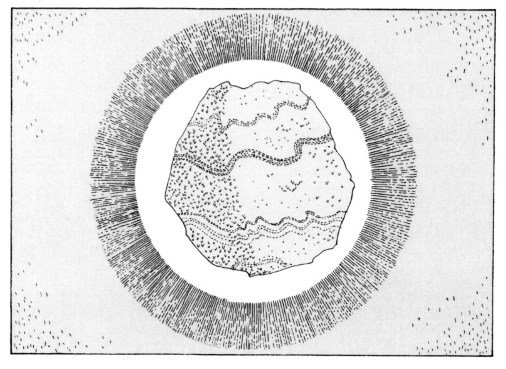

Like grains of sea salt

and sand finely dusting

all the sentimental moods

that surface when our friendship

comes to mind,

you give shape

to the timid wind. Full and brilliant

as the harvest moon, a little lion curled up cozy in the sky,

you

deserve it all: your motherhood,

the ache of your fingers

pressing your guitar,

your dreams pulled

down from clouds

and planted now

as promises kept,

as beauty born

from bruised knees,

as pain transliterated

to the best possible life,

frozen seeds

now aromatic

as your

most

beloved rose.

for Meredith

WHATEVER HAPPENED TO THE BLUE WHALE IN 2302 AD? WORDS RUSSELL JONES, PICTURES EDWARD ROSS

THE HORNETS ARE LIVID THIS SPRING.

WE LOCK THE WINDOWS, PULL THE BLINDS TO SHUT OUT THE DIN OF STINGERS

BEATING AGAINST THE GLASS.

ANOTHER WAVE'S COMING.

THE NEWS REMINDS US TO KEEP AS COOL AS WE CAN

BECAUSE THE NEXT FLARE WILL CUT THE ELECTRICITY.

WE CRANK THE AIR CON TO MAXIMUM, DROP A TAB OF ALKALINE TO SETTLE THE DRINKING WATER.

GRANDPA ROCKS IN THE CORNER, TELLING US ABOUT THE EONS HE SAILED THE BURNING SEAS,

HOW GOOD MEN   LOST THEIR SIGHT FOR US.

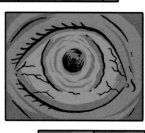

SUCH A SHAME, HE REPEATS, THERE'S NO MARINE TO TRAWL

NO BEACH TO HOLD OUR CASTLES, THAT RESERVOIRS ARE SCOTCH-BROTH-CONSISTENCY.

WE'VE STOPPED ASKING HOW THE OLD WORLD WAS

OR WHY HE WOULDN'T STOP CASTING WEIGHTED NETS

BURNING DOLLS' HEADS

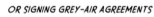

OR SIGNING GREY-AIR AGREEMENTS

WE GRIMACE AT HOW HE LIVES

IN THOSE DEAD DAYS

WON'T LET GO OF HEATHER AND HUMMING BIRDS AND MARMOSETS.

HE CALLS HIMSELF MAKAH, CAPTAIN AHAB, PINOCCHIO,

SHAKES A CRYSTAL BALL WHICH HOLDS

A LONG-GONE CITY,

ASH FLECKS SPIRALLING,

SETTLING ON THE TALL TIN ROOFS.

Generations lap the shore.

Motion. Out, bright peaks. A disequilibrated field.

In, spume, undertow.

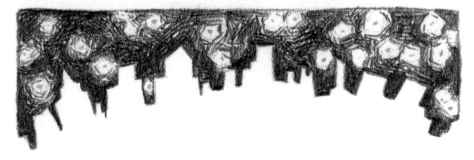

A coastline can't be drawn.

I am after   the permeable.
                              Dark surfaces

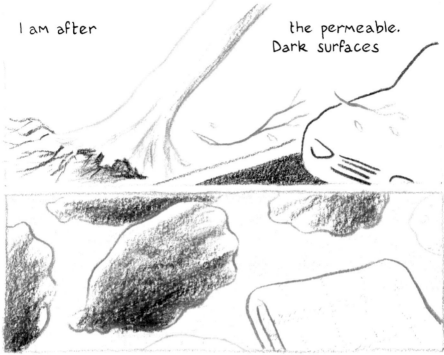

Motion: a word is ode, toward meaning

and you, sweet subject —dash me here

                    The world filtered
                 through me, through you.

REFLECTIONS

ANOTHER LIFE'S IMAGE
SHIMMERS ACROSS THE WATER
THE TIME TAKEN TO HEAL
SEEMS TO BE GETTING SHORTER

THEY TEASE ME INTO LOOKING
BLURRED COLOURS IMPLYING SHAPE
THEIR BEAUTY CATCHES ME A MOMENT
SERENITY NOW MY STATE

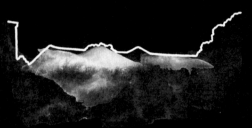

I DON'T CARE WHAT THEY WERE
AND NEITHER DOES THE RIVER
AS THE WIND ENGULFS THE BANK
THESE OUTLINES TURN TO SHIVER

THEN THE LAYERS COME OUT
THE BLUE, THE BROWN AND GREEN
I STUDY FOR A MOMENT
THERE'S A THOUSAND TO BE SEEN

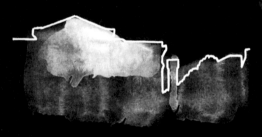
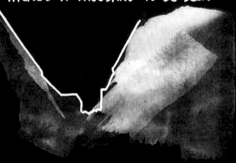

THE LONELY GREY OF THE ROCKS
LOOKS VIBRANT HERE AND FREE
I HEAR THE CALL OF THAT SUMMER
TRAPPED IN MEMORY

I'M TAKEN BACK WHEN I ANSWER
DRIFTING TO BLEAKER DAYS
THROUGH TO A DEEP DEPRESSION
BEFORE THE MANIC HAZE

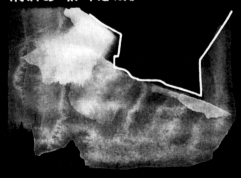

I CAN'T CONTROL THE WIND
OR THE TIDES ON WHICH I SAIL
MY BOAT SEEMS RUDDERLESS
THIS JOURNEY BOUND TO FAIL

WHAT WILL BE INEVITABLY IS
AND SOME WILL CALL IT FATE
EITHER WAY FOR ME
SALVATION WAS TOO LATE

THE GREY NOW LOOMS IN THE SKY
THE ROCK HAS LOOSENED ITS BIND
MORE MENACING AND BRUTAL
THE BLACK THAT LURKS BEHIND

FROM THERE THE ROUTE WAS GRIM
A SHADOW TAKING THE WHEEL
THROUGH HUMAN WASTELAND OR HELL
REALITY WAS TOO REAL

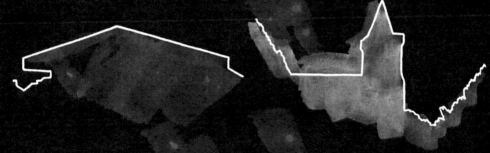

THEN LIFE JUST SNAPS ME OUT
DRAGGING ME BACK ASHORE
LIKE A NIGHTMARE IN REVERSE
THE BEGINNING HOLDS FEAR NO MORE

CATCHING ME ONCE AGAIN
AND TAKING THE HERE AND NOW
THE SHIMMERING REFLECTION OF THEN
BEAUTIFUL SOMEHOW

WRITTEN BY R.H. PARRY
DRAWN BY IOAN MORRIS

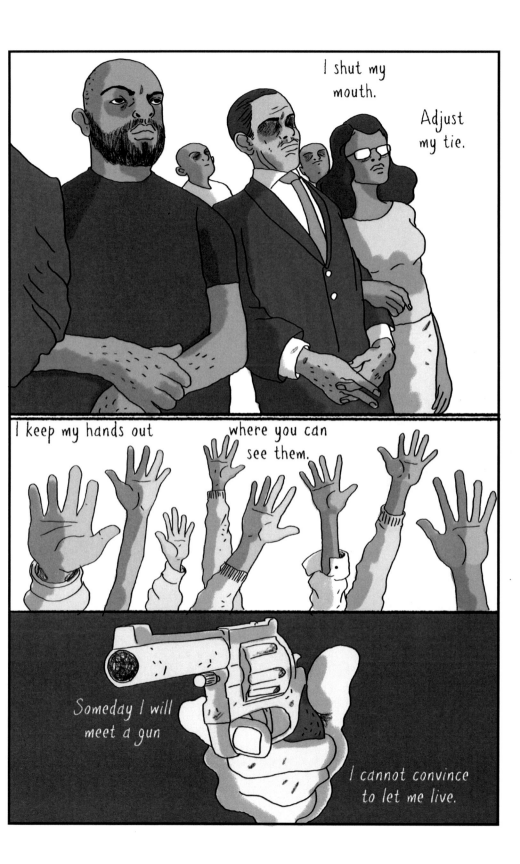

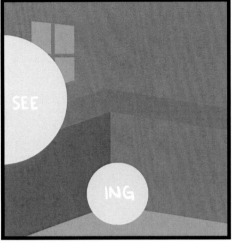

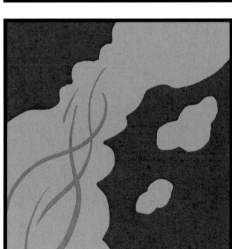

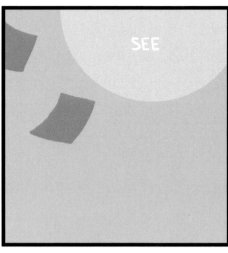

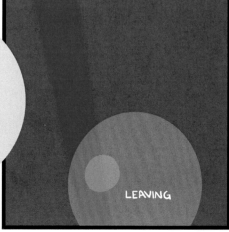

ANDREW WHITE

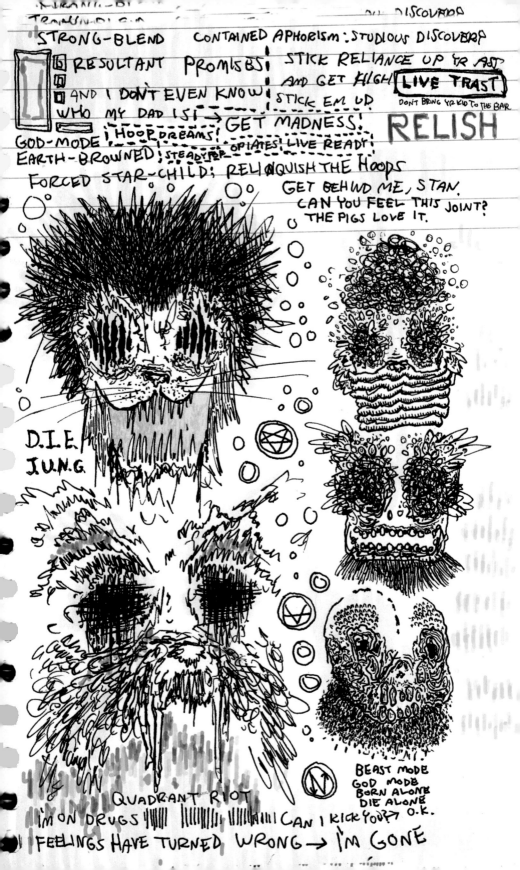

STRONG-BLEND   CONTAINED APHORISM: STUDIOUS DISCOVERY

RESULTANT PROMISES!   STICK RELIANCE UP YR ASS

AND I DON'T EVEN KNOW   AND GET HIGH   **LIVE TRAST**

WHO MY DAD IS! → GET MADNESS!   STICK EM UP   DON'T BRING YR KID TO THE BAR

¡HOOP DREAMS!   **RELISH**

GOD-MODE   OPIATES! LIVE READY!

EARTH-BROWNED! STEADY TP

FORCED STAR-CHILD; RELINQUISH THE HOOPS

GET BEHIND ME, STAN.
CAN YOU FEEL THIS JOINT?
THE PIGS LOVE IT.

D.I.E.
J.U.N.G.

QUADRANT RIOT

I'M ON DRUGS   CAN I KICK YOU? O.K.

BEAST MODE
GOD MODE
BORN ALONE
DIE ALONE

FEELINGS HAVE TURNED WRONG → I'M GONE

A SEA OF FACES IN THIS TOWN

A MESH OF MOODS THOUGHTS + FROWNS

EVERY DAY A FLOWING STREAM

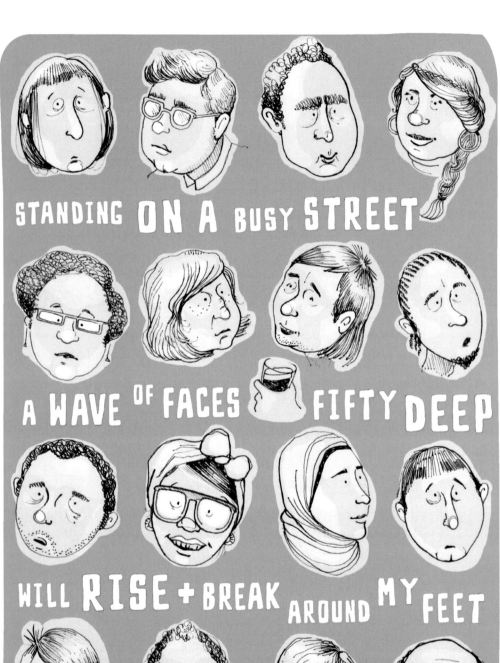

STANDING ON A BUSY STREET

A WAVE OF FACES FIFTY DEEP

WILL RISE + BREAK AROUND MY FEET

AN UNRECORDED SOUNDTRACK OF A SLEEPY CITY.

AN ELECTRIC WHITE NOISE.

AN AFTER-HOURS BUZZ.

AN UNTRANSLATABLE CHATTER.

SOMEWHERE A BELL RINGS QUIETLY.

THEN WE SAIL SLOWLY, STOP-START, THROUGH SOUTH LONDON STREETS.

Reading ourselves

in pictures

We look for stories

they might
be telling

But they have no stories
of their own

they
merely
reflect
OURS

Though sometimes they whisper

softly.

UV
DOUGLAS NOBLE

The sun booming

In shimmering skies

Over slowly

Burning skin

A shadow   Passes over

The sun booming   In shimmering skies.

POOL
by inechi

I've been pulling myself inside out
traveling the worlds within me

I dip my fingers
into a thousand pools of thought

just to play with
the reflection of light

ALL PROBLEMS ARE THE SAME PROBLEM

BY CONOR STECHSCHULT

JennyRobins.com
Life's a
DING-DONG!
Love
Potion
Never content
with
THE LINE OF
BEST FIT
Persist and persevere,
There's nothing to stop you now.
hold onto your hat
NICE TO MEET YOU
TWINKLE
TWINKLE
WILD
BEASTS
FLY
All Aboard
Broken Dream
RHAPSODY
an
Unlikely
I'M TOO OLD FOR THIS
(MAYBE)

I'VE BEEN THINKING, YOU KNOW, LITTLE BIRD, ABOUT THE UPPER FLOOR OF MY GRANDFATHER'S HOUSE. HE HARDLY EVER WENT THERE, COULDN'T REALLY FACE THE STAIRS. THE CLOSETS WERE ALL HALF-OPEN. I REMEMBER THE PHOTO-GRAPHS. I MEAN, I CAN'T SEE THEM, BUT I REMEMBER THEM.

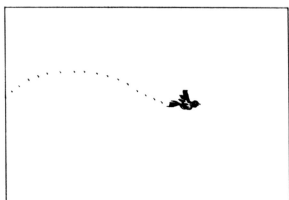

I WAS AWAY WHEN HE DIED. I COULDN'T
HELP WITH THE EMPTYING-OUT. WHEN
I THINK OF IT, I SEE IT AS IF I'M A
CHILD, FROM WAIST-HIGH. SOMETIMES
I LIKE TO THINK THAT THE BACKS
OF ALL THE CLOSETS IN THE
WORLD ARE JOINED TOGETHER.

the Practical Application of Colour

ALIZARIN CRIMSON

BURNT UMBER

HAUNTED

The little girl who ate buttercups is haunted
The Gold Lion and the two Red Lions are haunted
Following the death of a dog, the driver of a car and its two passengers, the zebra crossing at the infant's school is haunted

1...2...3...4...

The old wooden bus shelter near the gated park is rumoured to be haunted
Under the pier, at the high tide mark, is haunted
The dog known as 'Handsome' haunts the perimeter of the library

The butcher's father, Ted the elder, forbade the making of beef sausages following the death of a customer in 1973 who subsequently haunts the butchers
Discarded pistachios shells under cinema seats are haunted

The Liberal Club is haunted by a cat called 'Jinx' who will drink shandy, but only from an ashtray

Penelope Caldwell, daughter of the last Town Crier, haunts the civic centre
The last Town Crier haunts the now derelict toilet block of the private Boys' School
Persons unknown haunt the 377 bus route

The defunct ticket machine in the delicatessen is haunted
Constance Bown, lifetime companion of Penelope Caldwell, haunts the duck pond
The trees by the new roundabout are haunted, though they've mostly been cut down

If you have the urge to swallow pebbles it is a ghost
If when you close your eyes you can remember your first taste of butter it is a ghost
If your cat paws the place you were sitting when you leave the room your cat is a ghost
If you lie in bed emphatically alone you are a ghostly presence
If you can't see a ghost but can see yourself very small it is most definitely a ghost

END

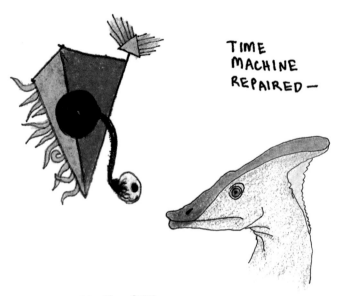

TIME
MACHINE
REPAIRED —

OFF TO SPY
ON HADROSAURS

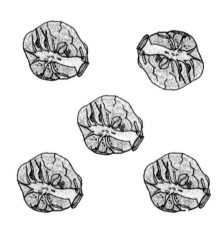

DINNER'S IN
THE FRIDGE

SHORT HOP——
——DESHAN TENNEKOON

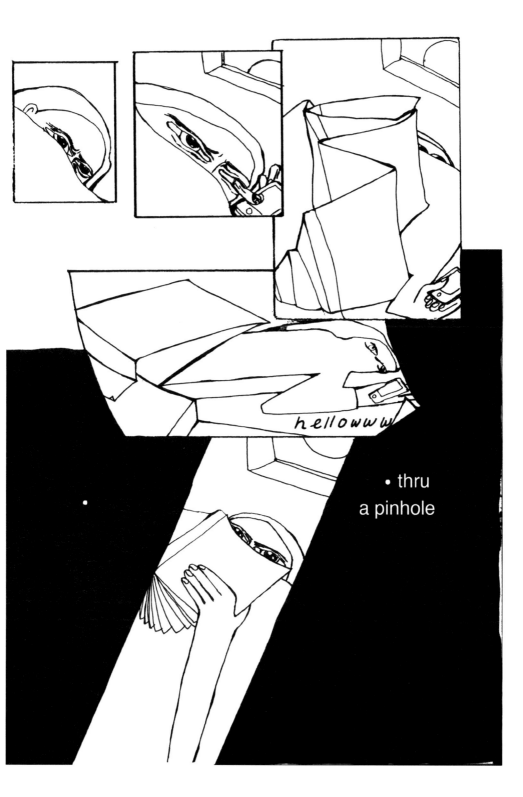

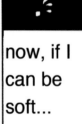

now, if I
can be
soft...

I WANT TO SQUEEZE YOU TIL MY SKIN COMES OFF

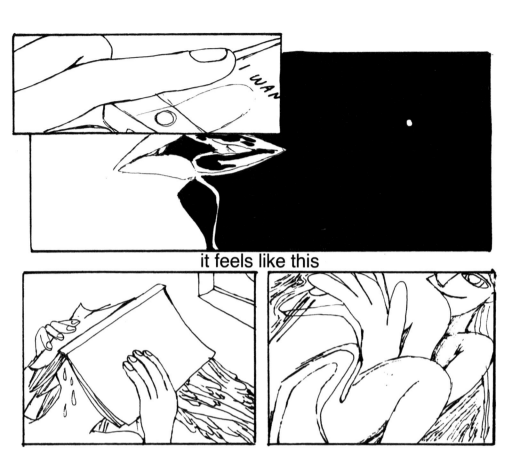

it feels like this

ok I gotta go

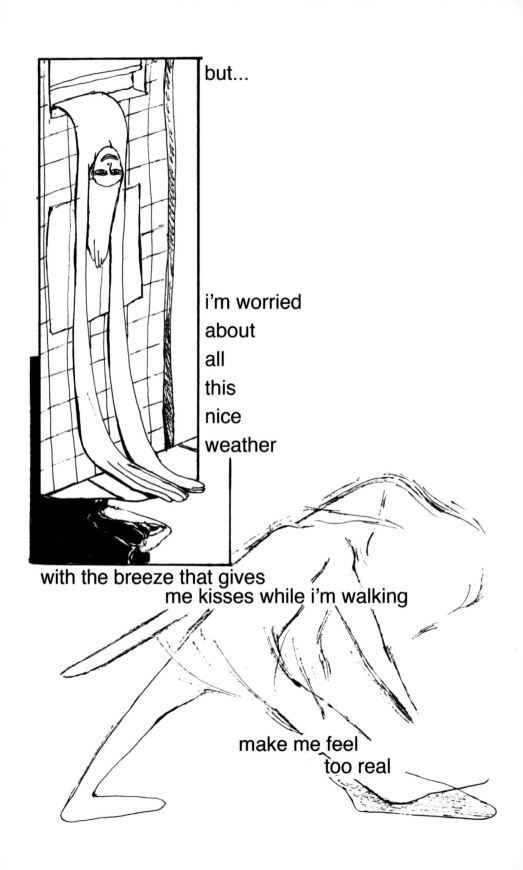

i get cloudy

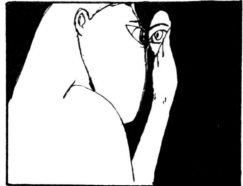

so it's hard to see

LALA 2015

I AM POWER. I AM UGLY
AND BEAUTIFUL AT THE
SAME TIME.

NOT ONE OR THE OTHER.

THE OPPOSITE OF LOVE IS OBLIVION.

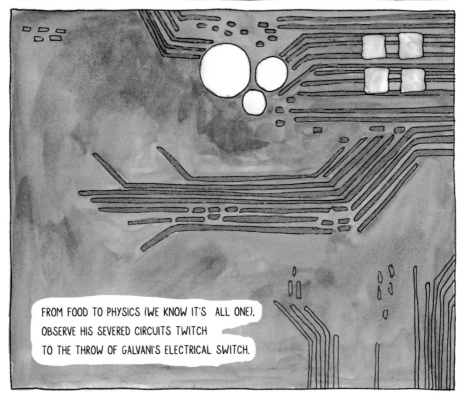

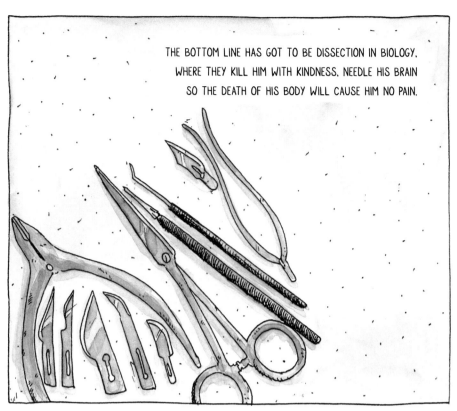

THE BOTTOM LINE HAS GOT TO BE DISSECTION IN BIOLOGY,
WHERE THEY KILL HIM WITH KINDNESS, NEEDLE HIS BRAIN
SO THE DEATH OF HIS BODY WILL CAUSE HIM NO PAIN.

PHILOSOPHY IS FORCED UPON THE FROG.
HE KNOWS FROM EXPERIENCE THAT DEATH WON'T GO AWAY,
THAT HE WILL CROAK TOMORROW IF HE DOESN'T CROAK TODAY.

STUDY GROUP

Nobody reads me now

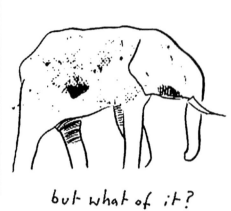

but what of it?

Ah, those launch parties

those women

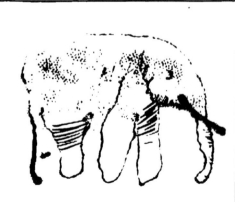

their gentle hands.

Monday night terrors.

By John Canfield and Sean Azzopardi

A slim somewhat familiar silhouette

Catalyses cackle and cry

divides itself between darkness and dawn

infiltrates the fault-lined floorboards.

Limbs are pinned with paralysis.

the heart rate is hand cranked.

Entirely black is better

than a grey that gives

the cover for malevolence to multiply.

Eyelids snap open to see

asleep and awake are exactly the same.

slipping
out

SLIPPED

Rebecca Truscott-Elves

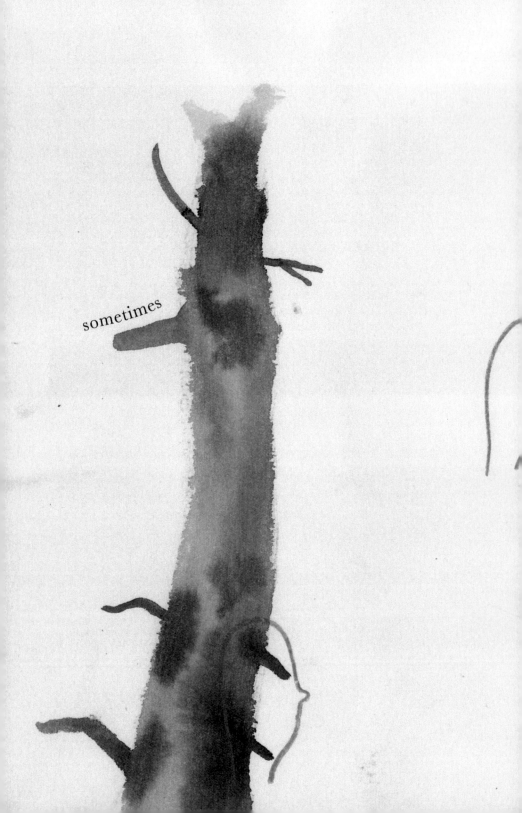

sometimes

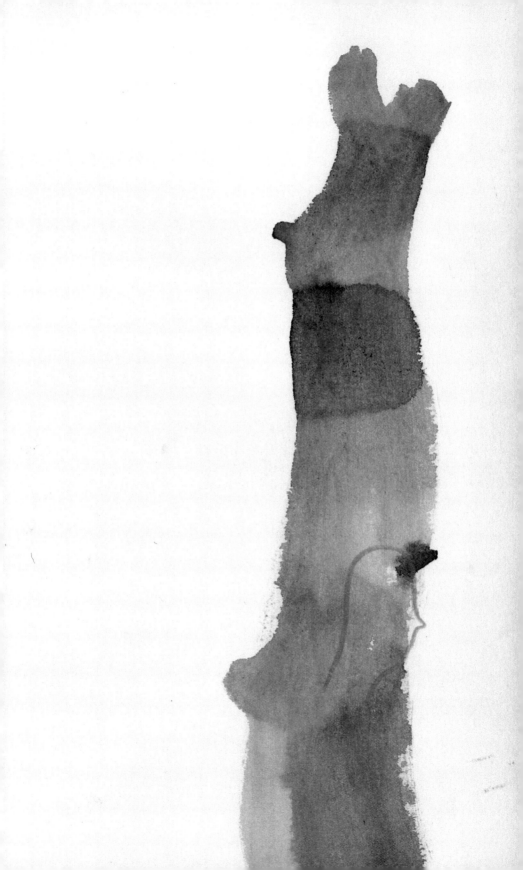

you'll find
me,

sometimes,
you won't.

iii. contributors and acknowledgments

Protoliths
Emix Regulus

Emix (@origamiship) draws comics inspired by inner states and outer space. She lives in Walthamstow, London.

microcosmic-orbit.com

Meredith
Trinidad Escobar

Trinidad is an Oakland-based cartoonist and poet. She has an MFA Comics degree from CCA.

trinidadescobar.com

Whatever Happened to the Blue Whale in 2302 AD?
Russell Jones and Edward Ross

Russell is an Edinburgh-based writer. He has published four collections of poetry and writes YA novels.

poetrusseljones.com

Edward is an Edinburgh-based comic creator, author of the graphic novel *Filmish — A Graphic Journey Through Film*.

edwardross.co.uk

Triborough Bridge
Alexander Rothman

Alexander is a cartoonist and poet, and publisher of *Ink Brick*, a micro-press dedicated to comics poetry.

inkbrick.com

Leaving
Andrew White

Andrew's comics explore the overlap between narrative and abstraction. He was born in 1990 and lives in Virginia, USA.

whitecomics.net

Reflections
R H Parry and Ioan Morris

Rhydian is the author of *Reflections*. He lives and works in Brecon.

Ioan is a cartoonist and musician based in Cardiff. You can find poetry zines by Mr Parry and comics by Mr Morris at their website.

drycomics.bigcartel.com

Breakable
Ivy Alvarez and Cristian Ortiz

Ivy is the author of *Disturbance*, and the pamphlets *Hollywood Starlet* and *The Everyday English Dictionary*.

ivyalvarez.com

Cristian (@bitsofcrom) is a London-based comic book artist and creator of the comic book series *Golden Campaign*.

cristianortiz.com

Relish
Rio Aubry Taylor

Go forth and subsist on pain. Follow xir on Twitter @RioAubryTaylor. See xir latest work at:

jettycomics.com

Sea of Faces
Anna Saunders

Anna is a London based Artist and Illustrator. Her work can be seen in *Solipsistic Pop.*

annasaundersdrawings. blogspot.co.uk/

Cold Coffee
Hayley Fiddler

Hayley is a poet, illustrator and fine artist from Oxfordshire.

facebook.com/hayleysart

Nightbus
Tim Bird

Tim (@t_j_bird), author of *Grey Area* and *Infrastructure*, lives and works in south London.

timothybird.co.uk

Reading Ourselves
Nicolas Labarre

Nicolas (@labarren) lives, teaches, draws comics and writes children's books in Bordeaux, France.

UV
Douglas Noble

Douglas was raised in The Borders.

strip-for-me.com

The Pool
Inés Estrada

Inés is from Mexico City and currently lives in Texas, USA. Her comics have been published by *Vice, Breakdown Press* and *Kus!.*

inechi.com

All Problems are the Same Problem
Conor Stechschulte

Conor is the author of *The Amateurs* and *Generous Bosom*. He lives and works in Chicago.

conorstechschulte.com

Ding Dong
Jenny Robins

Jenny (@jennyrobins) is an illustrator based in London. Work includes the series *What Birds are Really Thinking* and *Real TV Wisdom.*

jennyrobins.com

The Hills
David Troupes

David (@davidtroupes) is a poet and cartoonist publishing with Two Ravens Press and Carcanet.

buttercupfestival.com

What are you Doing?
Shauna Robertson

Shauna messes around with words and pictures in a small Gloucestershire studio near the source of the Thames.

Cathedral
Joseph Turrent

Joseph lives in South East London with his wife and children.

@turrentula

The Practical Application of Colour
Chris McCabe and Sophie Herxheimer

Chris (@mccabio) is a poet, writer and cemetery obsessive.

chris-mccabe.blogspot.co.uk

Sophie (@herxideas) draws and writes in ink with a brush most days.

sophieherxheimer.com
poetryteapot.wordpress.com

Haunted
Amy Key and Rob VonRamm

Amy (@msamykey)'s book *Luxe* was published in 2013. Her poems have appeared in *POETRY*, *The Poetry Review* and elsewhere.

amyvkey.com

Rob (@robvonramm) is a Brighton-based illustrator and creator of the webcomic series *Surviving Brighton*.

robvonramm.com

Short Hop
Deshan Tennekoon

Deshan lives on a tropical island. He had a pet mango but his children ate it.

100daysofpodi.tumblr.com

Thru a Pinhole
Lala Albert

Lala lives and works in Brooklyn, NY.

plslala.com

False Positive
Cody Pickrodt

Cody is a journalist, cartoonist and illustrator. His serial comic *Reptile Museum* is published by Ray Ray Books.

Slipped
Rebecca Truscott-Elves

Rebecca (@rebeccaelves) is an illustrator with sidelines in taking trains halfway across the world and writing.

rebeccaelves.com

Philospophy is Forced Upon the Frog
Roderick Hart and Zuzanna Dominiak

Roderick (@roderick_hart) is
a writer of poems and novels.

roderickhart.net

Zuzanna (@zuzuofcomics) is an
illustrator and comic artist based
in Edinburgh.

zyzanna.com

Study Group
Lorraine Mariner and Oliver East

Lorraine (@lorrainemariner) is a
poet based in London. Her most
recent collection is *There Will Be
No More Nonsense*.

Oliver is the writer/artist of
Trains Are...Mint and *Swear Down*,
amongst others. He lives and
works in Manchester, UK.

olivereast.com

Wasp Securities
W.N. Herbert and John Aggs

W.N. Herbert (@billherbert)
author of *Omnesia* (Bloodaxe,
2013), lives and works in
Newcastle and Dundee.

wnherbert.wordpress.com

John has drawn graphic novel
adaptations for Philip Pullman,
Robert Muchamore and Malorie
Blackman's *Noughts and Crosses*.

johnaggs.com.

Monday Night Terrors
John Canfield and Sean Azzopardi

John Canfield (@johncanfield_)
grew up in Cornwall and now
lives, works, writes and drinks in
London.

Sean (@seanazz) lives in London
and makes and publishes comics.

sean-azzopardi.com

thanks

We are immensely grateful to Arts Council England for giving us a grant to help produce this book. It allowed us to hold an open call for submissions which introduced us to the work of many artists who were previously unknown to us, and it allowed us to pay them. We are also grateful to Sidekick Books for taking on this project with such enthusiasm.

Thanks are due to Alexander Rothman for his advice, as well as to the raft of curious people who have supported and encouraged this book, whether from the beginning, or as the result of an exchange of exciteable emails from strangers. Also to Mike Sims at the Poetry Society, who planted the idea of applying for funding in the first place, without which this book might never have happened. Its publication was accompanied by exhibitions at both the Poetry Society's Poetry Cafe and the Saison Poetry Library in London, to whom we are also indebted.

The editors would also like to thank their partners, Becky and Kieron, for their patience.

acknowledgments

The comics extracts on pp10-12 are from the rather excellent *Understanding Comics* by Scott McCloud (Tundra, Paradox Press, Kitchen Sink, 1993; HarperCollins, 2004). Warren Craghead's piece *If a Note Next to a Note* on p22 was originally published on http://www.thethepoetry.com. The original poem 'Poem for a bus shelter' by Clare Shaw on p26 appears in *Straight Ahead* (Bloodaxe Books, 2006).

about the editors

Chrissy Williams
is a writer, critic and tutor based in London, UK. She is the author of various works of poetry, including *Flying into the Bear* (HappenStance Press, 2013, shortlisted for Michael Marks Award), and collaborations with visual artists *The Jam Trap* (Soaring Penguin Press, 2012) and *ANGELA* with Howard Hardiman (Sidekick Books, 2013). Her work has been featured on BBC Radio 4. She is a Visiting Lecturer in Creative Writing at the University of Hertfordshire and has been running Poetry Comics groups and workshops in London for several years. She is also the editor of a number of comics, including the Eisner Award-nominated and British Comic Award-winning comic *The Wicked + The Divine*.

chrissywilliams.blogspot.com | @chrissywilliams

Tom Humberstone
is a comic artist and illustrator based in London, UK. He produced the weekly political comic *In The Frame* for the *New Statesman*, which was nominated for a British Comic Award in 2014. His comics have been published by Image Comics, Cartoon Movement, The Nib, and Blank Slate Books. He also edits and publishes the UK comic anthology *Solipsistic Pop*.

tomhumberstone.com | @TomHumberstone